To Tracy, for being my Muse and Inspiration.
To Doreen Lee, the first and best editor I ever had.
And to Fosco El Doggo, for keeping me sane.

T. L.

To the memory of my mother,
Daniela, to my light Ariane and
to the next generation of pirate
women, Kaya and Lara.

S. H.

This is a work of fiction. Names, characters, places and incidents
are either the product of the author's imagination or, if real, are used
fictitiously. All statements, activities, stunts, descriptions, information and
material of any other kind contained herein are included for entertainment
purposes only and should not be relied on for accuracy or replicated as
they may result in injury.

First published 2019 by Walker Books Ltd
87 Vauxhall Walk, London SE11 5HJ

10 9 8 7 6 5 4 3 2 1

Text © 2019 Tony Lee
Illustrations © 2019 Sam Hart

Coloured by Tarsis Cruz with Flavio Costa

Lettered by Cadu Simões

The right of Tony Lee and Sam Hart to be identified as author and
illustrator of this work has been asserted by them in accordance with the
Copyright, Designs and Patents Act 1988.

This book has been typeset in CCWildWords

Printed in China

British Library Cataloguing in Publication Data:
a catalogue record for this book is available from the British Library

ISBN 978-1-4063-4735-7

www.walker.co.uk

Pirate Queen

THE LEGEND OF GRACE O'MALLEY

Pirate Queen

THE LEGEND OF GRACE O'MALLEY

WRITTEN BY
TONY LEE

ILLUSTRATED BY
SAM HART

COLOURED BY
TARSIS CRUZ WITH **FLAVIO COSTA**

LETTERED BY
CADU SIMÕES

WALKER

he Irish Rebellion against Henry VIII led by Silken Thomas, the Earl of Kildare, has failed, and the leaders have been executed.

Henry VIII is now the uncontested King of Ireland, and Irish lords are expected to surrender their lands to the throne in the hope that they will be given them back for their loyalty.

Many never see their lands again.

The Irish are forced to follow the English Tudor rule, under which their churches are ransacked, their language ignored, their people oppressed. English lords are given Irish lands, and Irish clans find that their claims of succession fall on deaf ears.

But there is a storm coming.

In Connacht, Ireland, the Chieftain Eoghan Dubhdara Ó Máille, known in legend as Dubhdara O'Malley has a daughter, Gráinne Ní Mháille – better known as Gráinne Mhaol, or Granuaile. And this girl will one day bring the fight to the English, become a thorn in the side to Queen Elizabeth herself, and become a legend in the process.

For there is indeed a storm coming – and her name is Grace O'Malley, the Pirate Queen of Ireland...

I NEED TO LEAVE TOMORROW FOR *SPAIN* – WE NEED TO PREPARE FOR THE SUMMER TRADING.

TAKE ME WITH YOU, DA'! TEACH ME THE WAYS OF THE SEA!

YOU'RE FIFTEEN, GRACE. YOU'RE ALMOST A WOMAN.

YOU NEED TO BE LEARNING A WOMAN'S SKILLS. NOT SAILING AROUND THE WORLD.

A WOMAN'S SKILLS? *NEEDLEWORK AND DANCING?*

I'M AN O'MALLEY! WE DON'T DANCE!

YES, YOU'RE AN O'MALLEY. YOU BRING THE STORMS AND LAUGH FIRE.

BUT UNLESS WE TURN ENEMIES TO ALLIES, THE ENGLISH WILL TAKE *EVERYTHING* WE'VE BUILT OVER THE YEARS.

COME, GRACE, WE NEED TO RETURN TO THE KEEP...

THE *O'FLAHERTY CLAN* WILL HAVE ARRIVED BY NOW.

THE O'FLAHERTYS? I *HATE* THEM!

THEIR SON'S A FOOL!

THE GREAT HALL OF THE O'MALLEYS.

DUBHDARA! YOU HAVEN'T AGED A DAY!

AND YOU LIE LIKE AN ENGLISHMAN, GILLEY!

SO, HAVE YOU THOUGHT OVER OUR OFFER?

I HAVE, AND IT'S A MIGHTY TEMPTING ONE.

I NEED TO THINK ABOUT IT STILL — BUT YOU SHALL HAVE MY ANSWER WHEN I RETURN FROM SPAIN.

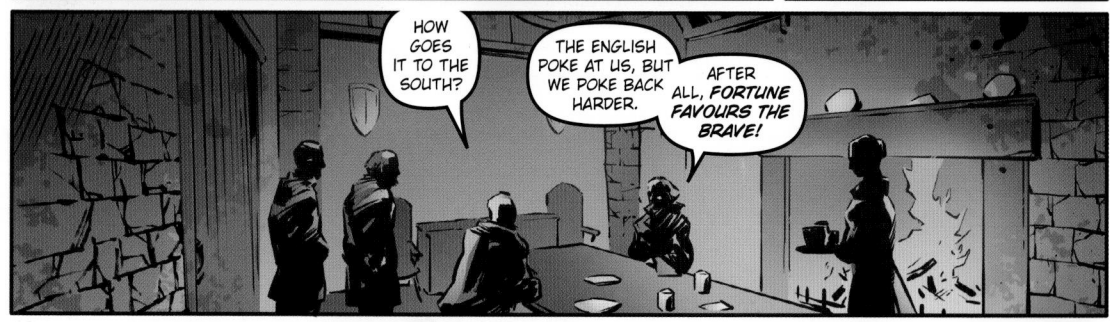

HOW GOES IT TO THE SOUTH?

THE ENGLISH POKE AT US, BUT WE POKE BACK HARDER.

AFTER ALL, FORTUNE FAVOURS THE BRAVE!

LIVING YOUR LIVES BASED ON A MOTTO ISN'T THE BEST WAY...

CLANG!

WHAT'S THAT NOISE? IT SOUNDS LIKE FIGHTING!

IF YOU'VE DOUBLE-CROSSED US, GILLEY—

I SWEAR! I KNOW NOTHING ABOUT THIS.

THAT NIGHT.

HEY! YOU! WHERE DO YOU THINK YOU'RE—

... GRACE?

I'M SORRY, DONAL — BUT I'M GOING WITH MY DA' TO SPAIN. I DON'T WANT TO STAY HERE.

DOES HE KNOW?

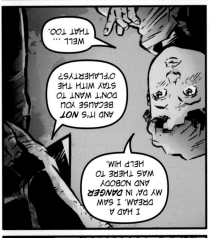

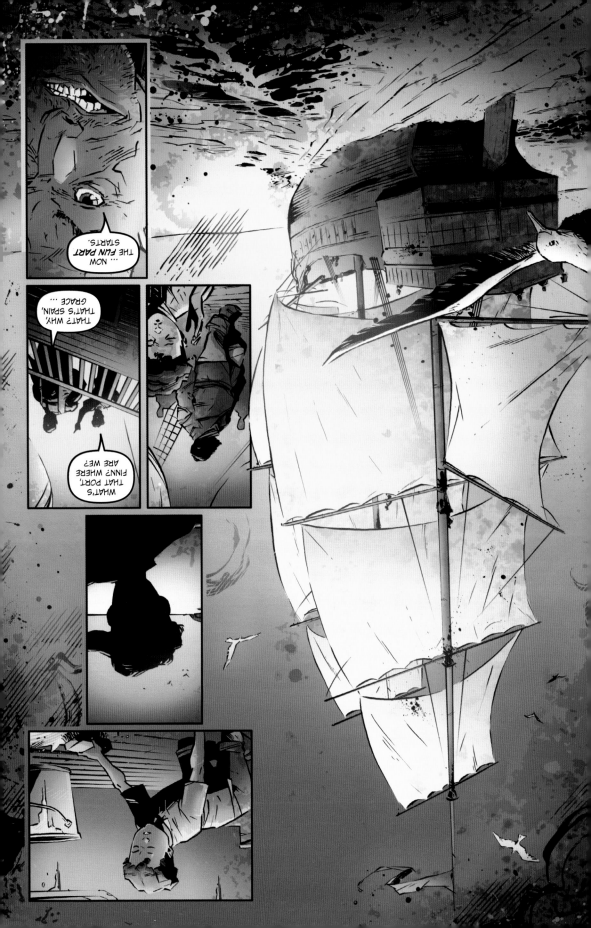

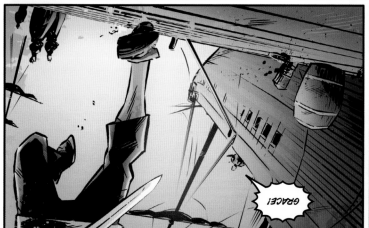

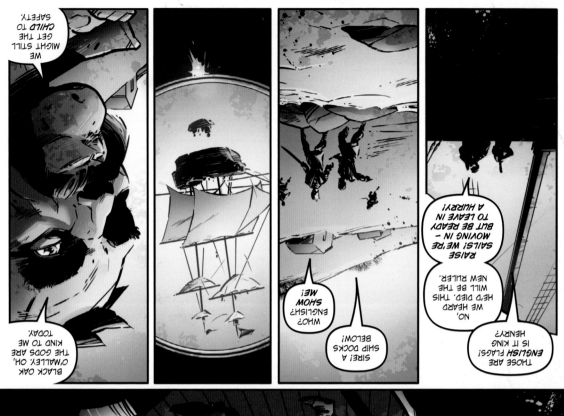

CONNACHT – HOME OF
DONAL AND GRACE.

LORD DONAL!
YOU **DON'T** WANT
TO GO IN THERE
TODAY!

THE LADY'S
IN A FOUL
MOOD!

WHAT'S
SHE
DOING NOW? CAN
A MAN GET NO
REST?

I'M SICK OF
NEEDLEWORK AND
WEARING DRESSES!
YOU CAN'T MAKE
ME, DONAL
O'FLAHERTY!

I'M YOUR **HUSBAND**,
GRACE! AND YOU'RE A
CHIEFTAIN'S WIFE!
YOU NEED TO **ACT**
LIKE ONE!
NO MORE
BATTLES! NO MORE
FIGHTS! STOP **PIRATING**
THE ENGLISH SHIPS AND
LOOK AFTER OUR
CHILDREN!

THAT'S
ALL I DO! GIVE
YOU BABIES AND
LOOK AFTER
THEM!

OWEN!
MARGARET!
MURROUGH! DO YOU
EVEN REMEMBER
THEIR NAMES?

OF COURSE
I DO! I CAN'T
HELP THE FACT THAT
I'M **CHIEFTAIN**! I
GET BACK WHEN
I CAN!

THE ENGLISH
ARE AT OUR
DOOR – WE
HAVE TO FIGHT!

I KNOW –
IT'S JUST ...

... I'M NOT
THIS WOMAN, NO
MATTER WHAT YOU
WANT. I'M A SAILOR,
NOT A MOTHER.

I KNOW,
GRACE. BUT THE
CHILDREN NEED YOU.
AND MY **PEOPLE** NEED
A LADY WHEN
THE LORD
IS AWAY.

WEAR
WHAT YOU
WANT, I DON'T
CARE...

AND TO
THINK YOU
SAID YOU
LOVED ME.
LIAR.

KNEW
IT THE DAY I
GAVE YOU MY
SWORD.

Self-checking guide 1

=0	=1	=2	=3	=4
10-10				
	10-9			
	9-8	10-8		
	8-7	9-7	10-7	
	7-6	8-6	9-6	10-6
5-5	6-5	7-5	8-5	9-5
	5-4	6-4	7-4	8-4
	4-3	5-3	6-3	7-3
	3-2	4-2	5-2	6-2
	2-1	3-1	4-1	5-1
	1-0		3-0	

How to play Snap

1. Shuffle the cards and deal all the cards equally amongst the players.

2. Keeping the cards face down, players take it in turns to turn over their top card and place on a pile in the middle.

3. When two consecutive cards match, the first player to call 'Snap!' will win the pile of cards. For example

9-2 and 8-1

4. This player then starts a new pile in the middle by turning over their top card.

5. If two players call 'Snap!' at the same time, or if an incorrect call is made, play continues until there is a clear winner.

6. The winner is the player left with all the cards.

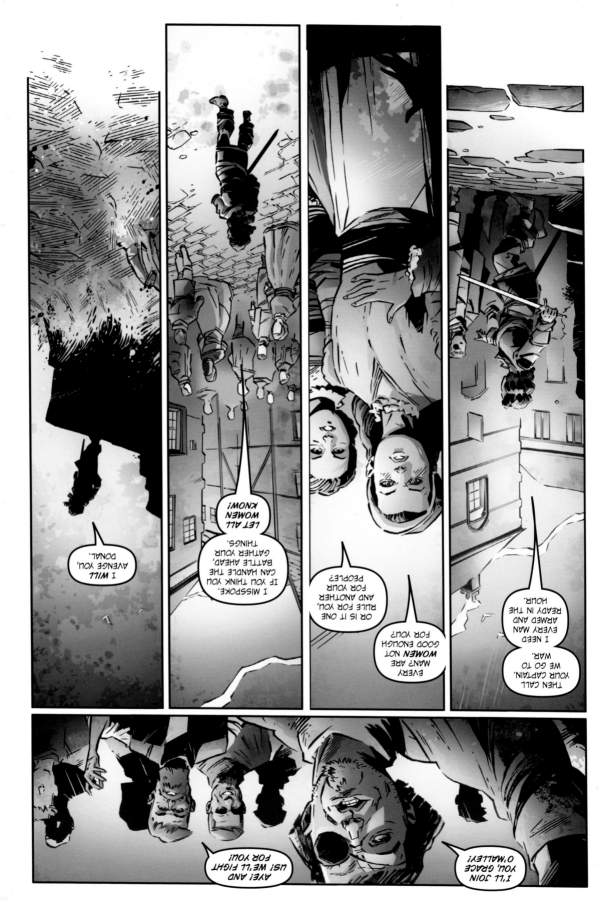

WE'RE ALL PACKED, MA'AM.

ARE YOU SURE YOU WANT TO LEAVE?

THERE'S NOTHING BUT *MEMORIES* HERE FOR ME NOW.

I'M NOT THE CHIEFTAIN, AND MY CHILDREN ARE TOO YOUNG TO CHALLENGE THE ENGLISH. WE MUST GO BACK TO SAFER GROUND.

THE ENGLISH WANT ME *DEAD*. THEY'LL COME HERE SOON. SO I HAVE TO LEAVE.

YOU'RE WELCOME TO COME WITH ME, BACK TO CLARE ISLAND, BUT IT'S O'MALLEY LAND.

IF YOU WISH HOWEVER TO LEAVE, THEN DEPART AS FAMILY.

WE'LL BE LEAVING YOU TONIGHT, LADY GRACE. I NEVER FOUND MY SEA LEGS.

THE LIFE OF A PIRATE WAS NEVER FOR ME.

WE HEAR THAT *RICHARD BURKE* IS RAISING AN ARMY AGAINST THE ENGLISH. I RECKON THAT'S WHERE WE'LL GO.

SOME OF THE JOYCES ARE COMING WITH US. WE'D WELCOME YOU *TOO*, IF YOU EVER CHANGE YOUR MIND.

RICHARD OF THE IRONS? I KNOW HIM. A GOOD MAN, EVEN IF HE'S A SCOUNDREL.

TELL HIM TO TREAT YOU WELL, OR HE'LL HAVE THE *PIRATE QUEEN* TO ANSWER TO.

SAFE JOURNEY, O'FLAHERTYS AND JOYCES.

MAY YOUR SHIP SAIL STRAIGHT, GRACE O'MALLEY.

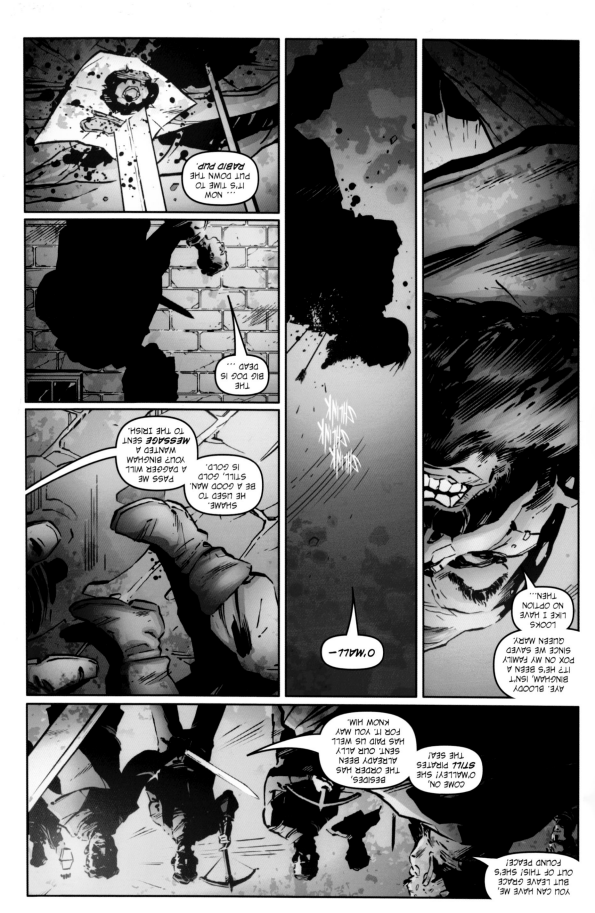

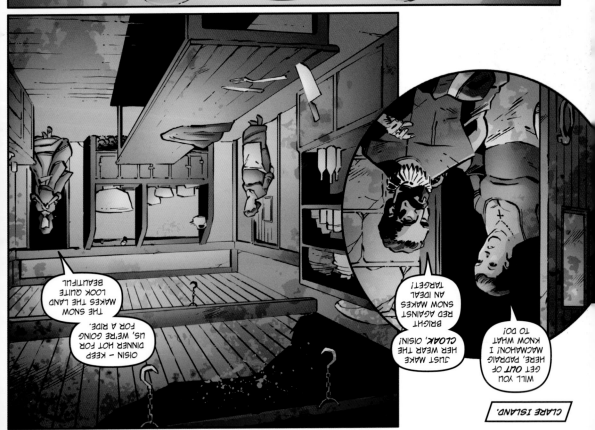

CLARE ISLAND.

ROCKFLEET CASTLE – HOME OF RICHARD BURKE.
I'M SORRY TO HEAR OF YOUR FATHER'S DEATH, GRACE. I KNOW YOU TOOK REVENGE ON THE MACMAHONS ...
... BUT THE **REAL** KILLERS WILL BE BROUGHT TO JUSTICE.
THE **REAL** KILLERS ARE IN **ENGLAND**, RICHARD, SO I'LL HAVE TO DO WITH KILLING ALL THE ENGLISH I CAN FIND.
I'M NO **SOLDIER,** THOUGH. I PROPOSE A JOINT AGREEMENT.
A **MARRIAGE**. A YEAR AND A DAY. I GAIN ROCKFLEET CASTLE, AND YOU GAIN THE **O'MALLEY FLEET**.
BETWEEN US WE CAN SECURE WESTERN IRELAND FROM THE ENGLISH. MY PEOPLE WILL BE SAFE.
I GET YOUR FLEET **AND** YOUR HAND IN MARRIAGE? WHAT FOOL WOULD TURN THAT DOWN?
DONE! WE WED LATER TODAY!
YOU'LL TAKE THE **BURKE** NAME, OF COURSE.
OVER MY DEAD BODY, HUSBAND.

CRASH!

DAMN THAT WOMAN! WHY WON'T SHE DIE!

YOU HAVE TO GIVE HER CREDIT. SHE'S DONE WONDERFULLY SINCE YOU TRIED TO KILL HER. THE *FIRST* TIME, THAT IS.

AND NOW SHE KNOWS YOU KILLED HER FATHER...

IT WAS SUPPOSED TO *BREAK HER!* NOT *INSPIRE HER!*

AND NOW SHE'S ALLIED WITH *BURKE!* PREGNANT WITH HIS CHILD AND *STILL* PIRATING OUR SHIPS!

LOOK, RICHARD OF THE IRONS IS *NOTORIOUS* FOR HIS AFFAIRS. AFTER A YEAR AND A DAY THEY'LL SPLIT...

YOU THINK SHE *CARES*? THIS MARRIAGE IS A SHAM! SHE GIVES HIM A CHILD, HE GIVES HER WESTERN IRELAND!

THEY'LL SPLIT AT A YEAR AND A DAY, PROBABLY FOR THE REASONS YOU SAY...

... BUT IT'LL BE A *PLAY*, PERFORMED FOR AN AUDIENCE.

WE'LL THINK THEM FRACTURED, AND THAT'S WHEN THEY'LL ATTACK *HARDER*.

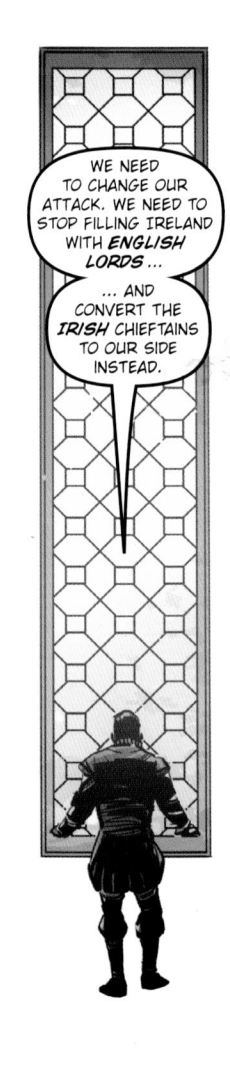

WE NEED TO CHANGE OUR ATTACK. WE NEED TO STOP FILLING IRELAND WITH *ENGLISH LORDS*...

... AND CONVERT THE *IRISH* CHIEFTAINS TO OUR SIDE INSTEAD.

THE IRISH SEA.

CAPTAIN O'MALLEY! WE'RE UNDER ATTACK!

YOUR BROTHER'S BEEN HURT.

OH.

ARE YOU *MAD*, BOY! CAN'T YOU SEE YOUR CAPTAIN IS *GIVING BIRTH*?

ARGHHH!!

BOY! WHERE IS YOUR CAPTAIN!

GET HER TO *SURRENDER* THE SHIP!

I'M SORRY – I CAN'T LET YOU IN RIGHT NOW.

COULD YOU COME BACK LATER?

TO *BLAZES* WITH THIS! *GRACE O'MALLEY!* BY ORDER OF THE—

SHLUNK

WWAAAAAAAHHHHHH!!

IS THAT A *BABY*?

KIDNAPPING MY SON? THIS IS *NO WAY* FOR AN IRISH NOBLEWOMAN TO ACT!

BUT AS YOUR GUARD SAID, I'M *NOT* A NOBLEWOMAN. I AM AN *OUTLAW* IN YOUR EYES. BANNED FROM YOUR HEARTH.

REFUSED HOSPITALITY.

WHAT DO YOU WANT ME TO DO? I CANNOT JUST LET *ANYONE* COME IN!

WHY NOT? MY FATHER WAS A CHIEFTAIN, AND EVERY DINNER HE ENSURED AN *EXTRA PLACE* WAS SET AT THE TABLE, IN CASE OF UNEXPECTED GUESTS.

IN FIVE YEARS WE ONLY EVER SAW *ONE*. BUT IT DIDN'T MATTER.

THE POINT WAS THAT EVERYONE *KNEW* THAT MY FATHER'S HEARTH WAS THERE FOR WHOEVER NEEDED IT.

THE GATES OPEN TO FRIENDLY VISITORS. A MEAL SET ASIDE AT THE TABLE. HOSPITALITY GIVEN.

DO YOU KNOW WHO THAT ONE GUEST *WAS*, EARL OF HOWTH?

YES. IT WAS *ME*. A WINTER, TWENTY YEARS AGO, IF I RECALL CORRECTLY.

IF HE HADN'T OPENED HIS HEARTH THAT NIGHT I WOULD HAVE DIED.

BUT I CANNOT ALLOW YOU ENTRY TO THE CASTLE. THE ENGLISH—

CAN BE *DAMNED*. THIS ISN'T ABOUT ME, THOUGH. THIS IS ABOUT THE LAWS OF *HOSPITALITY*.

THIS IS ABOUT YOU REMEMBERING YOUR *HERITAGE*.

FROM NOW ON, YOUR GATES ARE OPEN FOR *ANYONE* WHO NEEDS TO SPEAK TO YOU.

AND EACH NIGHT YOU'LL PUT AN *EXTRA PLACE* AT YOUR TABLE, JUST IN CASE OF UNEXPECTED GUESTS.

NO ONE SHOULD FEEL THE SHAME I DID WHEN TURNED AWAY.

YOU'RE RIGHT, OF COURSE. I AGREE.

NOW RELEASE MY SON—

OH, YOUR SON WAS NEVER A PRISONER. HE FEELS THE SAME WAY I DO.

THAT'S WHY HE EATS HIS DINNER IN A *TAVERN*, THOMAS!

THOMAS! I THOUGHT I'D *LOST* YOU!

IF YOU'D KEPT TRYING TO BE LIKE AN *ENGLISH* LORD, FATHER, YOU WOULD HAVE.

ONCE MORE I OWE AN O'MALLEY FOR SAVING MY LIFE, IT SEEMS.

NOTHING MORE THAN A SMALL GUIDING PUSH.

CAP'N! WE GOT *THREE SHIPS* COMING! ENGLISH!

AS PLEASURABLE AS THIS WAS, GENTLEMEN, THE LAST THING I WANT THE ENGLISH TO SEE IS YOU ON MY DECK.

REALLY? I THOUGHT YOU'D BE *HAPPY* TO SEE MORE WAR BETWEEN US!

NO. THERE WILL BE **NO NEGOTIATIONS** WITH THE LIKES OF GRACE O'MALLEY.

YOU CANNOT SPEAK LIKE THAT TO THE *QUEEN*! IT'S TREASON!

NO, IT'S TREASON TO KEEP HER *FROM* THE TRUTH! IRELAND WON'T BOW TO US UNTIL WE *BURN IT TO THE SOIL*!

I'M A SOLDIER. I FIGHT FOR THE CROWN.

I FOUGHT FOR *HENRY*. I FOUGHT FOR *MARY*. I EVEN FOUGHT FOR *LADY JANE* IN THE WEEK OR SO THAT SHE WAS QUEEN.

AND NOW I FIGHT FOR QUEEN ELIZABETH. AND YOU KNOW WHAT I'VE LEARNED IN THOSE YEARS?

THAT KINGS AND QUEENS COME AND GO, BUT DEATH AND THE O'MALLEYS ARE *ALWAYS* THERE.

STOP TRYING TO *COLONIZE* THE IRISH. *EXTERMINATE* THEM INSTEAD.

KINGS AND QUEENS MAY COME AND GO, BUT THIS QUEEN STILL *COMMANDS* YOU.

YOU ARE MY SOLDIER? YOU WANT TO FIGHT?

UM, WELL, THAT IS...

THEN YOU CAN FIGHT IN *CYPRUS*.

AND YOU CAN STAY THERE UNTIL YOU LEARN HOW TO *ADDRESS ME IN THE CORRECT MANNER*.

THE CELLS UNDER DUBLIN CASTLE.

GRACE O'MALLEY. THE PIRATE QUEEN, *FINALLY* WHERE SHE BELONGS.

A LUCKY BREAK IN BAD WEATHER, NOTHING MORE. SOON I'LL BE BACK ON THE OCEAN.

WHERE'S MY SON, *OWEN?* THEY TOOK HIM FROM ME WHEN WE ARRIVED HERE.

HE TRIED TO ESCAPE. THERE WAS AN ACCIDENT.

YOUR SON IS *DEAD.*

YOU *LIE!*

OH, IT'S ALL TRUE. AND THE FUNNIEST PART OF IT IS THAT WE KNEW WHERE YOU WERE BECAUSE YOUR *OTHER* SON, MURROUGH *TOLD* US.

SEEMS HE'S SICK OF BEING IRISH. WANTS TO CHANGE SIDES. GOOD PLAN.

OH, OWEN... OH, MURROUGH... WHAT HAVE I DONE TO YOU...

WELL, I THINK THAT'S *OBVIOUS.* YOU DRAGGED THEM INTO A FUTILE WAR AGAINST A BIGGER OPPONENT.

YOU'RE GOING TO *DIE,* O'MALLEY. YOU'RE GOING TO BE *HANGED* FOR THE TRAITOR YOU ARE. AND THEN WE'LL KILL BURKE AND YOUR OTHER SON.

WHO KNOWS? WE MIGHT EVEN KILL MURROUGH FOR THE *SHEER HELL* OF IT.

COUNTY MEATH, IRELAND.

WHAT *HAPPENED* HERE? THE WHOLE VILLAGE HAS BEEN BURNED TO THE GROUND!

THOMAS OF HOWTH SAID THAT BINGHAM HAD *GIVEN* UP ON BRIBING CHIEFTAINS.

NOW HE *KILLS* THEM, BURNING THEIR VILLAGES TO THE GROUND. *SCORCHED EARTH.*

CHILDREN DIED HERE. WHAT KIND OF MAN COULD DO THAT?

AN *ENGLISH* MAN.

NO. I'VE MET *MANY* ENGLISHMEN OVER THE YEARS. NOT ONE OF THEM WOULD DO SOMETHING LIKE THIS!

THIS BINGHAM IS A *MONSTER!*

AYE, THAT HE IS. AND THE SOONER WE *REMOVE* HIM, THE SOONER WE HAVE A CHANCE OF SAVING IRELAND.

COME ON, I HEAR THE FAINT SOUNDS OF *BATTLE.* I THINK WE'VE FOUND RICHARD.

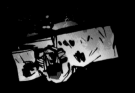

MY FIGHTING IS DONE.

I HAVE FOUGHT FOR DECADES – FOR NOTHING MORE THAN BLOOD AND SORROW.

I APPRECIATE IT, BUT I HAVE LOST MY FATHER, MY SON, A LOVER AND TWO HUSBANDS TO THE ENGLISH.

WHAT ABOUT YOU, GRACE O'MALLEY? WE'LL FOLLOW YOU!

YEAH! PIRATE QUEEN! PIRATE QUEEN!

RICHARD IS DEAD.

YOU NEED TO ELECT A NEW CHIEFTAIN. ONE THAT ISN'T TIED TO THE ENGLISH. YOU NEED TO KEEP FIGHTING.

YOU NEED TO COST THE ENGLISH FOR EVERY YARD OF IRISH LAND THEY STEAL.

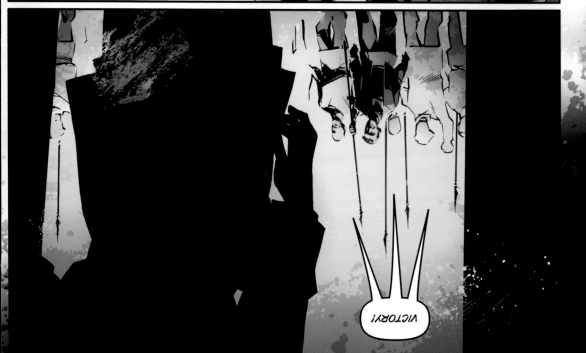

VICTORY!

IT'S FROM ENGLAND. YOUR BROTHER AND YOUR SONS ARE LOCKED IN THE *TOWER OF LONDON*.

RICHARD BINGHAM HAS REQUESTED YOU GIVE YOURSELF UP AND *JOIN* THEM, OR THEY'LL BE EXECUTED.

AND IF I JOIN THEM?

IT DOESN'T SAY.

I FOUGHT FOR IRELAND FOR TWO DECADES, BUT AFTER RICHARD DIED THEY ELECTED AN *ENGLISH PUPPET* AS THE MACWILLIAM, THE HIGH CHIEFTAIN.

I WALKED AWAY FROM BATTLE AND STILL BINGHAM HOUNDS ME.

DAMN MURROUGH! I TOLD HIM *TO LEAVE IT BE!*

HE'S HUNTED FOR BINGHAM ON THE SEAS FOR A YEAR AND HE'S *NEVER* KNOWN WHAT TO DO WHEN HE FOUND HIM!

WHAT MESSAGE SHALL I SEND BACK?

WRITE TO BINGHAM. TELL HIM THAT WE'LL MEET ON THE *OPEN SEAS* TO DISCUSS THIS.

AND THEN I WANT YOU TO WRITE SOME OTHER LETTERS.

THE IRISH SEA.

I'M GLAD YOU KEPT TO YOUR SIDE OF THE AGREEMENT, BINGHAM. ONE SHIP, ONE CREW.

NOW, I'D LIKE TO DISCUSS THE *OPTIONS* I HAVE TO FREE MY KINSMEN.

THERE ARE NO OPTIONS. YOU'RE UNDER ARREST FOR *TREASON*, YOU AND YOUR WHOLE CREW!

AND HOW ARE YOU GONNA ARREST US, ENGLISHMAN? YOU'RE ONLY ONE SHIP!

YES, I MIGHT HAVE *LIED* ABOUT THAT.

CAPTAIN! *TWO MORE ENGLISH SHIPS* APPROACHING!

YOU *DOUBLE-CROSSED* US! WE CAME HERE IN GOOD FAITH!

YES! AND I'D DO IT A HUNDRED TIMES AGAIN IF IT MEANT THAT I'D STOP YOUR *PIRACY* ON THESE SEAS!

MY ARMADA IS APPROACHING. YOU HAVE NO CHANCE! SURRENDER!

OH, I DON'T THINK SO.

YOU SEE, I THOUGHT THAT YOU'D DO THIS.

MISS GRACE O'MALLEY OF IRELAND.

YOUR MAJESTY, BY THE GRACE OF GOD.

YOU BOW DOWN TO ME? IS THIS HOW QUEENS ARE *SUPPOSED* TO MEET?

I AM NO QUEEN, MA'AM. IT WAS A NICKNAME GIVEN TO ME.

I AM JUST A *MOTHER*, FIGHTING FOR THE LIVES OF HER CHILDREN.

YOUR WORDS DO YOUR EXPLOITS INJUSTICE. THE QUEEN OF PIRATES IS NOT A NICKNAME TO TAKE LIGHTLY.

NOR IS THE FACT THAT YOU CONSTANTLY *DEFY* ME.

I DEFY INVADERS TO MY HOME, YOUR MAJESTY. INVADERS THAT *BURN VILLAGES DOWN* AND *KILL CHILDREN*.

MY APOLOGIES – SNIFF – IT WAS A COLD JOURNEY AND I FEEL I HAVE CAUGHT A SLIGHT CHILL.

HERE, TAKE MY HANDKERCHIEF.

THANK YOU.

I SAY! HOW RUDE!

WE NEED TO GET *OUT OF HERE!* THE STORM'S ENDING ...

... THE OTHER SHIP WILL BE BACK!

LOOKS LIKE YOU GET TO *LIVE* TODAY, BINGHAM. TODAY I SPARE YOUR LIFE.

YOUR MEN WILL HAVE A *CHOICE* — HUNT AND KILL US, OR GET YOU TO A DOCTOR.

NO! I WON'T OWE MY LIFE TO YOU! *KILL ME!*

I DARE YOU!

HAVE A NICE LIFE, RICHARD.

I'M SURE WE'LL SEE EACH OTHER AGAIN.

LOOKS LIKE THEY CHOSE THE *SECOND* OPTION

LUCKY FOR US.

I HAVEN'T HAD A CHANCE TO SAY IT YET, BUT *THANK YOU*, MA.

AFTER EVERYTHING I'VE DONE, TO COME AND SAVE ME...

YOU'RE *KIN*, MURROUGH. OF COURSE I'D SAVE YOU.

BESIDES, YOU HAD *TIBBOT* AND YOUR *UNCLE DONAL* ON YOUR SHIP ...

... AND I LIKE THEM *MORE* THAN YOU.

MOTHER!

COME ON, LET'S GET HOME.

LET'S ENJOY THE PEACE WHILE IT LASTS.

LONDON.

SIR RICHARD, IT HAS BEEN A **WHILE** SINCE YOU GRACED OUR PRESENCE AT COURT. YOUR INJURY HEALS?

AS WELL AS IT CAN, YOUR MAJESTY. BY THE GRACE OF GOD I LIVE, AND THAT IS ENOUGH FOR ME.

I MUST ADMIT, I DO FIND IT **STRANGE** THAT IMMEDIATELY AFTER **GAINING PARDON** FOR HER FAMILY AND LEAVING COURT ...

... THE FIRST THING SHE DOES IS HUNT YOU DOWN AND **SKEWER** YOU.

NOT QUITE THE ACTIONS OF A WOMAN WHO WANTS **PEACE,** WOULD YOU SAY?

I AGREE, MA'AM. AND THIS IS THE REASON WE MUST **CONTINUE** OUR PURGE OF IRELAND ...

... THEIR PEOPLE **CAN'T BE TRUSTED** TO NEGOTIATE WITH!

I MIGHT NOT AGREE WITH YOUR **METHODS,** SIR RICHARD, BUT YOU DID BRING ME RESULTS.

RETURN TO YOUR DUTIES, BUT WITH A **LIGHTER HAND** THIS TIME.

THEY WON'T EVEN KNOW THAT I'M THERE, YOUR MAJESTY.

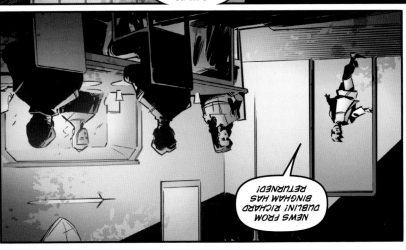

... IT'S TIME TO **DEFEND OUR LANDS** AGAIN.

THE O'MALLEYS FOUGHT THE ENGLISH AGAIN THROUGHOUT THE NINE YEARS WAR. GRACE O'MALLEY **NEVER STOPPED** DEFENDING HER HOMELAND.

SHE DIED, AGED **73** IN 1603, AT HER HOME, SURROUNDED BY HER FAMILY. IT WAS THE SAME YEAR THAT **QUEEN ELIZABETH I** DIED.

TONY LEE

Tony Lee has written for many popular comic books including *X-Men*, *Doctor Who*, *Spider Man*, *Starship Troopers*, *Wallace & Gromit* and *Shrek*. His adaptation of *Pride & Prejudice & Zombies: The Graphic Novel* was a #1 *New York Times* bestseller. He is also the author of the graphic novels *Outlaw: The Legend of Robin Hood*, *Excalibur: The Legend of King Arthur* and *Messenger: The Legend of Joan of Arc*, and adapted Anthony Horowitz's bestselling series *The Power of Five* into graphic novels. Tony lives in London. Find him online at tonylee.co.uk and on Twitter as @mrtonylee.

SAM HART

Sam Hart has illustrated many comic books and graphic novels, including *Judge Dredd, Starship Troopers, Outlaw: The Legend of Robin Hood, Excalibur: The Legend of King Arthur* **and** *Messenger: The Legend of Joan of Arc*. **His graphic novel** *The Coldest City,* written by Antony Johnston, has recently been adapted for the screen as *Atomic Blonde* starring Charlize Theron. He also works with newspaper and magazine illustration and advertising storyboards, and teaches drawing skills at the AXIS School of Art in Sao Paulo, Brazil, where he lives. Find him online at samhartgraphics.com, on Twitter as @samhart73 and on Instagram as @samrahart.

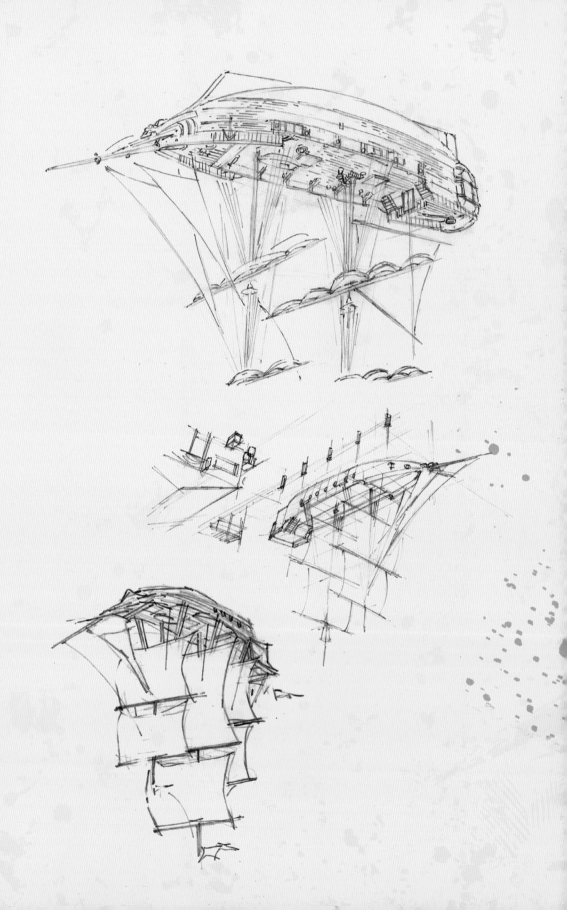

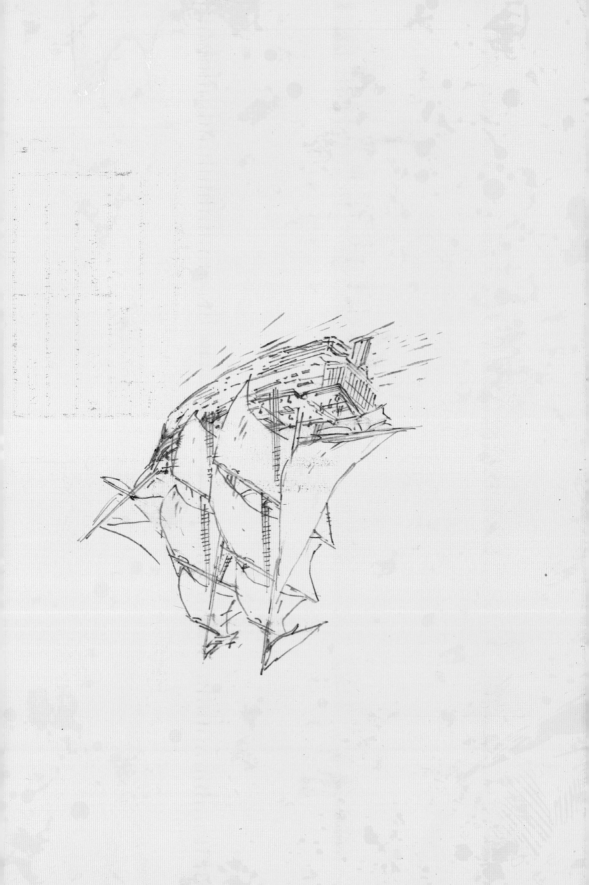